Women in t  t

STUDY GUIDE

Catherine Upchurch

LITTLE ROCK SCRIPTURE STUDY
Little Rock, Arkansas

THE LITURGICAL PRESS
Collegeville, Minnesota

DIOCESE OF LITTLE ROCK

2500 North Tyler Street • P.O. Box 7239 • Little Rock, Arkansas 72217 • (501) 664-0340 • Fax (501) 664-6304

Dear Friends in Christ,

The Bible comes to us as both a gift and an opportunity. It is a gift of God who loves us enough to communicate with us. The only way to enjoy the gift is to open and savor it. The Bible is also an opportunity to actually meet God who is present in the stories, teachings, people, and prayers that fill its pages.

I encourage you to open your Bibles in anticipation that God will do something good in your life. I encourage you to take advantage of the opportunity to meet God in prayer, study, and small-group discussion.

Little Rock Scripture Study offers materials that are simple to use, and a method that has been tested by time. The questions in this study guide will direct your study, help you to understand the passages you are reading, and challenge you to relate the Scriptures to your own life experiences.

Allow the Word of God to form you as a disciple of the Lord Jesus. Accept the challenge to be "transformed by the renewal of your mind" (Romans 12:2). Above all, receive God's Word as his gift, and act upon it.

Sincerely in Christ,

✠ J. Peter Sartain
Bishop of Little Rock

Sacred Scripture

"The Church has always venerated the divine Scriptures just as she venerates the body of the Lord, since from the table of both the word of God and of the body of Christ she unceasingly receives and offers to the faithful the bread of life, especially in the sacred liturgy. She has always regarded the Scriptures together with sacred tradition as the supreme rule of faith, and will ever do so. For, inspired by God and committed once and for all to writing, they impart the word of God Himself without change, and make the voice of the Holy Spirit resound in the words of the prophets and apostles. Therefore, like the Christian religion itself, all the preaching of the Church must be nourished and ruled by sacred Scripture. For in the sacred books, the Father who is in heaven meets His children with great love and speaks with them; and the force and power in the word of God is so great that it remains the support and energy of the Church, the strength of faith for her sons, the food of the soul, the pure and perennial source of spiritual life."

Vatican II, Dogmatic Constitution on Divine Revelation, no. 21.

INTERPRETATION OF SACRED SCRIPTURE

"Since God speaks in sacred Scripture through men in human fashion, the interpreter of sacred Scripture, in order to see clearly what God wanted to communicate to us, should carefully investigate what meaning the sacred writers really intended, and what God wanted to manifest by means of their words.

"Those who search out the intention of the sacred writers must, among other things, have regard for 'literary forms.' For truth is proposed and expressed in a variety of ways, depending on whether a text is history of one kind or another, or whether its form is that of prophecy, poetry, or some other type of speech. The interpreter must investigate what meaning the sacred writer intended to express and actually expressed in particular circumstances as he used contemporary literary forms in accordance with the situation of his own time and culture. For the correct understanding of what the sacred author wanted to assert, due

attention must be paid to the customary and characteristic styles of perceiving, speaking, and narrating which prevailed at the time of the sacred writer, and to the customs men normally followed in that period in their everyday dealings with one another."
Vatican II, Dogmatic Constitution on Divine Revelation, no. 12.

Instructions

MATERIALS FOR THE STUDY

This Study Guide: Women in the New Testament

Bible: The New American Bible with Revised New Testament or The New Jerusalem Bible is recommended. Paraphrased editions are discouraged as they offer little if any help when facing difficult textual questions. Choose a Bible you feel free to write in or underline.

Commentary: *Women in the New Testament* by Mary Ann Getty, S.T.D., Ph.D. (The Liturgical Press) is used with this study. The assigned pages are found at the beginning of each lesson.

ADDITIONAL MATERIALS

Bible Dictionary: *The Dictionary of the Bible* by John L. McKenzie (Simon & Schuster) is highly recommended as a reference.

Notebook: A notebook may be used for lecture notes and your personal reflections.

WEEKLY LESSONS

Lesson 1—Women of Expectant Faith
Lesson 2—Women Changed by Jesus
Lesson 3—More Women Changed by Jesus
Lesson 4—Women of Prominence

Lesson 5—Women and Discipleship, Part I
Lesson 6—Women and Discipleship, Part II
Lesson 7—Women and Discipleship, Part III

YOUR DAILY PERSONAL STUDY

The first step is prayer. Open your heart and mind to God. Reading Scripture is an opportunity to listen to God who loves you. Pray that the same Holy Spirit who guided the formation of Scripture will inspire you to correctly understand what you read and empower you to make what you read a part of your life.

The next step is commitment. Daily spiritual food is as necessary as food for the body. This study is divided into daily units. Schedule a regular time and place for your study, as free from distractions as possible. Allow about twenty minutes a day. Make it a daily appointment with God.

As you begin each lesson read the assigned chapters of Scripture found at the beginning of each lesson, the footnotes in your Bible, and then the indicated pages of the commentary. This preparation will give you an overview of the entire lesson and help you to appreciate the context of individual passages.

As you reflect on Scripture, ask yourself these four questions:

1. *What does the Scripture passage say?*
   Read the passage slowly and reflectively. Use your imagination to picture the scene or enter into it.

2. *What does the Scripture passage mean?*
   Read the footnotes and the commentary to help you understand what the sacred writers intended and what God wanted to communicate by means of their words.

3. *What does the Scripture passage mean to me?*
   Meditate on the passage. God's Word is living and powerful. What is God saying to you today? How does the Scripture passage apply to your life today?

4. *What am I going to do about it?*
   Try to discover how God may be challenging you in this passage. An encounter with God contains a challenge to know God's will and follow it more closely in daily life.

THE QUESTIONS ASSIGNED FOR EACH DAY

Read the questions and references for each day. The questions are designed to help you listen to God's Word and to prepare you for the weekly small-group discussion.

Some of the questions can be answered briefly and objectively by referring to the Bible references and the commentary *(What does the passage say?)*. Some will lead you to a better understanding of how the Scriptures apply to the Church, sacraments, and society *(What does the passage mean?)*. Some questions will invite you to consider how God's Word challenges or supports you in your relationships with God and others *(What does the passage mean to me?)*. Finally, the questions will lead you to examine your actions in light of Scripture *(What am I going to do about it?)*.

Write your responses in this study guide or in a notebook to help you clarify and organize your thoughts and feelings.

THE WEEKLY SMALL-GROUP MEETING

The weekly small-group sharing is the heart of the Little Rock Scripture Study Program. Participants gather in small groups to share the results of praying, reading, and reflecting on Scripture and on the assigned questions. The goal of the discussion is for group members to be strengthened and nourished individually and as a community through sharing how God's Word speaks to them and affects their daily lives. The daily study questions will guide the discussion; it is not necessary to discuss all the questions.

All members share the responsibility of creating an atmosphere of loving support and trust in the group by respecting the opinions and experiences of others, and by affirming and encouraging one another. The simple shared prayer which begins and ends each small group meeting also helps create the open and trusting environment in which group members can share their faith deeply and grow in the study of God's Word.

A distinctive feature of this program is its emphasis on and trust in God's presence working in and through each member. Sharing responses to God's presence in the Word and in others can bring about remarkable growth and transformation.

THE WRAP-UP LECTURE

The lecture is designed to develop and clarify the themes of the lesson. It is not intended to form the basis for the group discussion. For this reason the lecture is always held at the end of the meeting. If several small groups meet at one time, the large group will gather together in a central location to listen to the lecture.

Lectures may be given by a local speaker. They are also available on audio- or video-cassette.

The ideal way to study the Bible is to immerse yourself daily in it. Study guides used in Little Rock Scripture Study are usually set up to follow a pattern of three questions a day. This study guide follows a slightly different pattern. Questions are grouped by topic rather than by day. Study a topic (or a person) a day, and you will be prepared for each weekly small-group discussion.

LESSON 1 Women of Expectant Faith

Matt 1–2; Luke 1:5-56; 2:1-52
Women in the New Testament, pages 1–41

Introduction

1. What personal interests have brought you to this study of women in the New Testament?

2. The Gospels of Matthew and Luke both include infancy narratives (Matt 1–2; Luke 1–2). According to the commentary, what are some of the major differences to notice when reading the two accounts?

3. What point is Luke making by setting up comparisons and contrasts between John the Baptist and Jesus (Luke 1:11-79; 2:34-35, 50-51)?

4. As you recall the stories of the birth of Jesus, what impressions do you have of the women involved? (Simply list words or phrases.)

Elizabeth (Luke 1:5-25, 36-37, 39-45, 57-66)

5. What does Luke mean in 1:6-7 that Elizabeth was righteous (just)? (See Gen 15:6; Job 1:1; Isa 11:4-5.) And barren? (See Gen 18:11-14; 25:21; 30:22-23; Judg 13:2-5; 1 Sam 1:5-6.)

6. In the story announcing the birth of John, Elizabeth is not addressed by the angel and only speaks once, in Luke 1:25. What does her one statement tell you about her role in the telling of the story?

7. What purpose does Luke have in noting Elizabeth's lengthy seclusion (1:24)? (See 1:36, 39-40.)

Mary at the Annunciation (Luke 1:26-37)

8. The angel Gabriel announced both the birth of John and of Jesus (1:11-19, 26-38).

   a) What was Gabriel's role prior to these New Testament announcements? (See Dan 8:15-19; 9:21-27.)

   b) Assuming Mary was familiar with Gabriel's previous announcements, what might she have been thinking or feeling when Gabriel appeared to her?

9. What is meant by saying Mary "found favor with God" (1:30)?

10. Describe a time in your life when it seemed God was telling you "do not be afraid" (1:30). (See Gen 21:17; Deut 20:3-4; Ps 27:1; Isa 12:2; 41:10; Matt 14:25-27.)

11. Make a list of the concerns Mary may have had as she pondered her pregnancy (1:31) and the identity of her son (1:32-35). What might have been hardest for her as a young woman?

12. Do you know of a situation where the impossible became possible (1:37)? (See Gen 18:14; Matt 19:23-26.) How can such a transformation affect your faith in God?

13. Like Mary, we are called to bear Christ in our world. (See 1 Cor 12:27; 2 Cor 5:20.) In what ways can you do this? And what concerns do you have?

14. What do you hear in Mary's response to God's plan (1:38) that encourages you to see her as a model?

Mary and Elizabeth at the Visitation (Luke 1:39-56)

15. Read carefully the words of Elizabeth in Luke 1:42-45. What can you learn about Elizabeth's faith that is inspiring to you?

16. Compare Mary's canticle (1:46-55) with the canticle of Hannah (1 Sam 2:1-10) and other Old Testament passages (Exod 15:16; Ps 89).

    a) Does it surprise you to see that the themes of celebration, justice, and fulfilled promises are originally found throughout the Old Testament?

    b) Which line of the canticle is most challenging to you? Why?

Anna (Luke 2:22-38)

17. Read the story of Mary and Joseph presenting Jesus in the Temple (2:22-38). (See Exod 13:2.)

    a) Did your own parents dedicate you in some way to the Lord?

    b) What life experiences have taught you the value of faithfully waiting for God (as did Simeon and Anna)? (See Luke 12:35-37; Exod 13:2; Ps 27:14; 40:1; 130:6; Lam 3:25.)

    c) Anna the prophet turned faithful waiting into thanksgiving and proclamation (2:36-38). When has God's answer to prayer given you a reason to spread the news?

18. At this time in your life, do you find it easiest to relate to Elizabeth, Mary, or Anna? Why?

LESSON 2   Women Changed by Jesus

Matt 9:18-26; Mark 1:29-31; 5:21-43;
Luke 4:38-39; 7:11-17; 8:14-15, 40-56; 13:10-17
Women in the New Testament, pages 43–84

Review

1. How did last week's wrap-up lecture shed new light on your own study of Mary, Elizabeth, and Anna?

The Widow of Nain (Luke 7:11-17)

2. What is the relationship between the story of the widow and her son in Luke 7:11-16 and the cure of the centurion's servant (7:1-10)?

3. The woman in Luke 7:12 is identified as a "widow" and now the mother of a dead son. What is the significance of these two descriptions? (See Exod 22:21-22; Ps 127:3-5; 1 Tim 5:3-5.)

4. Review some of the passages that speak about showing "pity" and then comment on any new insights about Jesus being "moved with pity" (7:13). (See Exod 2:5-6; Ps 72:13; Isa 49:10; Hos 1:7; Joel 2:18; Mark 1:40-41; Luke 10:29-33.)

5. In what sense is Jesus "a great prophet" when raising the widow's son (7:11-16)? (For examples, see 1 Kgs 17:8-24; 2 Kgs 8:7-8; Isa 38:1-6, 21.)

Jairus's Daughter (Matt 9:18f.; Mark 5:21f.; Luke 8:40f.)

6. Jairus is said to have fallen at the feet of Jesus and pleaded for his daughter's healing (Mark 5:22-23; Luke 8:41-42). Given the status of female children in the ancient Middle East, what do you make of the father's posture and plea?

7. The young daughter of Jairus is resuscitated without readers ever knowing her name or hearing from her (Matt 9:23-26; Mark 5:35-43; Luke 8:51-56). What does this tell you about the status of females on the one hand, and the focus of the story on the other hand?

8. How does each Gospel writer use the story of the girl's resuscitation (Matt 9:18f.; Mark 5:21f.; Luke 8:40f.) to reinforce his purposes in writing?

The Woman Healed of a Hemorrhage
(Matt 9:20-22; Mark 5:25-34; Luke 8:43-48)

9. Review the commentary's explanation of the relationship between holiness and cleanness or purity. How does this connection help you to make sense of the social status of the hemorrhaging woman (Mark 5:25-34; Luke 8:43-48)?

10. Identify the emphasis of each Gospel writer in the telling of the story of the woman with a hemorrhage (Matt 9:21-22; Mark 5:26, 33; Luke 8:43-48).

11. a) In what ways do we ostracize people without understanding their pain or what has caused it?

    b) Have you ever been afraid to approach God with a problem? How did you find courage?

12. List the elements in the stories of Jairus' daughter and the woman with a hemorrhage that make them good companion stories. (See commentary.)

Simon's Mother-In-Law
(Matt 8:14-15; Mark 1:29-31; Luke 4:38-39)

13. Read the three versions of this healing, paying close attention to the actions of Jesus (Matt 8:14-15; Mark 1:29-31; Luke 4:38-39). What kind of feelings do you have about him in each of the accounts?

14. When have you felt the power of intercessory prayer (Luke 4:38)? Were you the intercessor or the one who benefitted from the intercession of others? (See Jas 5:14-16.)

15. a) When has the resumption of your normal routine helped you enjoy restored health? Could that help to explain the significance of the woman waiting on Jesus and the others (Matt 8:15; Mark 1:31; Luke 4:39)?

    b) How could the woman's encounter with Jesus begin to change her status in her community?

A Crippled Woman Standing Erect (Luke 13:10-17)

16. How can we understand some of the Gospel references that associate spiritual bondage with illness (13:11)? (For examples, see Mark 1:23-27; 5:2-5; 9:17-18; Luke 9:38.)

17. Jesus encountered a woman "bent over," unable to stand erect (13:11, 13). When have you felt "bent over" from the weight of concerns, responsibilities, or problems? How did God intervene to help you stand up straight?

18. How was Jesus' understanding of keeping the Sabbath different from that of many of his contemporaries (13:14-17)? (See Exod 20:8-11; Isa 58:13-14; Matt 12:9-13; Mark 2:23-28; Luke 14:1-6.)

LESSON 3 More Women Changed by Jesus

Matt 15:21-28; Mark 7:24-30;
Luke 7:36-50; 23:26-48; John 4:4-42; 7:53–8:11
Women in the New Testament, pages 84–122

Review

1. What was your favorite Scripture story from the previous lesson? Why?

Syrophoenician Woman (Matt 15:21-28; Mark 7:24-30)

2. Considering the history of the "region of Tyre (and Sidon)," what impact is there in telling the story of the encounter between Jesus and a woman from that region (Matt 15:21-28; Mark 7:24-30)? (See Ps 83:8; Ezek 26; Joel 4:4-8.)

3. The woman's humility is a strength, not a weakness (Matt 15:25-27; Mark 7:26-28). What are some of the Bible's lessons about humility? (See 2 Chron 7:12-16; Prov 3:34; 22:4; Matt 11:29; 18:2-5; Luke 18:10-14; James 4:6-10; 1 Pet 5:5-7.)

4. a) What can we learn from the Syrophoenician woman about how to get a positive response from those in power?

   b) What does she teach you about how to approach God when you are in need?

The Samaritan Woman (John 4:4-42)

5. Why was Samaria an unwelcome place for Jews (4:4, 9)? Summarize the history that separated the Jews from the Samaritans. (See 1 Kgs 16:24-26; 2 Kgs 17:24-33; Matt 10:5-6.)

6. Why do we sometimes fail to recognize God and the gifts of God in our lives (4:10)? What are some of the obstacles?

7. Jesus teaches the woman about "living water" (4:10, 13-15) and "true worship" (4:20-24). What events in your life has God used to teach you about these things? (See Isa 55:1; Jer 2:13; John 7:37-38; Rev 22:17.)

8. John contrasts the concerns and response of the Samaritan woman (4:7-29, 39-42) with those of Jesus' disciples (4:27-38). At this time in your spiritual journey, do you identify more with the woman or the disciples?

9. Another contrast occurs between the Samaritan woman (4:4-42) and the previous story in John's Gospel, that of Nicodemus (3:1-21). Which story is the more challenging to you in terms of following Jesus?

A Woman Judged Forgiven (John 7:53–8:11)

10. What is the punishment prescribed in the Mosaic Law for male adulterers? For female adulterers (8:4-5)? (See Lev 20:10-12; Deut 22:22-27.)

11. In this scene at the Temple, what is Jesus' criteria for judgment and forgiveness (8:7)? What is your criteria?

12. Although the woman forgiven by Jesus is almost completely silent, what could she have been thinking and feeling as the scene unfolded (8:3-11)?

The Woman Who Showed Great Love (Luke 7:36-50)

13. How does Luke's version of the woman who anoints Jesus (7:36-50) illustrate that he has a different purpose than the other Gospel writers? (See Matt 26:6-13; Mark 14:3-9; John 12:1-8.)

14. a) What does Jesus see in the woman that Simon the Pharisee does not see (7:44-50)?

    b) How do you feel when another person sees something in you that is hidden from others or even from yourself?

15. Why have some readers of this account assumed that the woman's sin is sexual in nature? Is this a fair rendering or is it colored by our own cultural biases?

Daughters of Jerusalem (Luke 23:26-31, 48-49)

16. As Jesus walked toward his crucifixion, many people followed along: crowds, others on the way to be crucified, the guards, Simon of Cyrene, etc. What might have been different about the women who were part of the crowd, called "Daughters of Jerusalem" (23:27)?

17. How does Jesus turn the weeping of the women into a teaching moment (23:28-31)? (See 19:41-44; 21:23-24.)

18. Luke makes particular mention of the faithfulness of the women as they remained with Jesus even during his crucifixion and after. What can we learn from them about the importance of being present during the suffering of others?

LESSON 4   Women of Prominence

Matt 14:1-12; Mark 6:14-29; 27:15-23, 55-56; Luke 9:7-9;
Acts 5:1-11; 16:1-3; 18:2, 18, 26; Rom 16:3;
1 Cor 16:19; 2 Tim 1:5; 3:14-15; 4:19
Women in the New Testament, pages 123–162

Review

1. Review the women of the past two lessons whose lives were changed by Jesus. What are some words you would use to summarize the kinds of changes they experienced because of their encounters with Jesus?

Herodias and Her Daughter
(Matt 14:1-12; Mark 6:14-29; Luke 9:7-9)

2. How does each Gospel writer expand upon or manipulate the story of the execution of John the Baptist? (See Mark 6:14-29; Matt 14:1-12; Luke 9:7-9.)

3. In Mark's telling of the story (Mark 6:14-29), who possesses the most power, Herodias, Salome, Herod, or John? Why?

Pilate's Wife (Matt 27:15-23)

4. In your opinion what is Pilate's main concern in offering to turn over a prisoner during the feast of Passover (27:15, 18-26)? Releasing an innocent man? Popularity with the Jews? Avoiding a riot? Seeking justice? Appeasing his wife? Something else?

5. Pilate's wife is in a position of influence and still has no real power to change the situation for Jesus (27:19). How do you deal with situations where your beliefs do not get a fair hearing, or are not respected?

The Mother of Zebedee's Sons (Matt 20:20-28; 27:55-56)

6. a) What does the woman's posture tell you about the mother of the sons of Zebedee (Matt 20:20)?

   b) What do her words tell you about this woman (Matt 20:21)?

7. Matthew's Gospel stresses training in discipleship. What evidence is there that the Mother of Zebedee's sons learned the true meaning of following Jesus? (See Matt 27:55-56)

Sapphira (Acts 5:1-11)

8. The story of Sapphira and Ananias (5:1-11) follows directly after the story of Joseph Barnabas (4:36-37). In each case property was sold, and in each case money was given to the community. Were Sapphira and Ananias being punished for not giving all the money? For not telling the truth about the price of the property? For giving poor witness to the community about God's ability to provide?

9. What role does Sapphira play in the way things unfolded (5:1-2, 8-10)?

10. Is "honesty is the best policy" the lesson of this story? Or is it something deeper? How would you describe it?

11. What can Sapphira teach you about the need for community?

Lois and Eunice (Acts 16:1-3; 2 Tim 1:5; 3:14-15)

12. What family member has been most influential in your own spiritual journey? If not a family member, then who?

13. What challenges would Eunice have faced in raising her son in a religiously "mixed" marriage (Acts 16:1; 2 Tim 1:5)?

14. Evidently, Lois and Eunice introduced Timothy to the (Hebrew) Scriptures, and perhaps introduced him to Christianity (2 Tim 3:14-15).

    a) What does this tell you about the importance of Scripture? (See 2 Tim 3:16-17; Ps 119:105; Isa 40:8; 55:10-11.)

    b) About the possible status of women in the early church communities? (See Gal 3:26-29.)

**Prisca/Priscilla
(Acts 18:2, 18, 26; Rom 16:3; 1 Cor 16:19; 2 Tim 4:19)**

15. What might be indicated from the fact that Priscilla is mentioned first in four of the six times she and her husband are called by name?

16. Priscilla and her husband are reported to have been teachers of Apollos when he arrived in Ephesus fresh from his conversion (Acts 18:24-26). Have you ever been in the position to give further instruction to someone enthusiastic but perhaps a little misinformed about the faith? Explain.

17. Given Paul's reputation (some would say undeserved) as one who limited the roles of women, what do you make of his acknowledging with gratitude the apparent leadership of Priscilla (Rom 16:3)? (See 1 Cor 11:7-16; 1 Tim 2:11-15.)

18. Priscilla and Aquila share their ministry together. When have you seen marriage provide an opportunity for shared ministry?

LESSON 5   Women and Discipleship, Part I

Matt 27:55-61; 28:1-8; Mark 6:3; 15:40-41, 47; 16:1-9;
Luke 8:1-3; 24:1-12; John 19:25-27; 20:1-18
Women in the New Testament, pages 163–191

Review

1. How would you summarize from the last lesson what you learned about the way women used prominent positions?

Disciples

2. Consider the many ways discipleship is described in the New Testament. Which of these ways is easiest for you? Which is most difficult? (See Matt 16:24-25; Luke 14:26-27; John 8:31-32; 13:35; 14:15; 15:7-14.)

3. Generally when you put together a mental list of the disciples in the New Testament who do you usually include? Do women's names or women's stories come to mind immediately?

The Galilean Women

4. a) The Galilean women are first introduced as a group in Luke 8:1-3. In that passage, what seems to be their role?
   b) How does the role of the Galilean women change when reading the accounts which place them at the cross and tomb (Matt 27:55-61; 28:1-8; Mark 15:40-41, 47; Luke 24:1-12; John 19:25-27; 20:1-13)?

5. a) What indicators might lead some to believe that "Mary, the mother of James and Joses" is the biological mother of Jesus (Mark 3:21, 31-33; 6:3; 15:40; 16:3)? (See John 19:25-27.)
   b) How has church teaching through the centuries clarified the relationship between James, Joses, and Jesus? (See commentary footnote.)
   c) How do we know that biology is not the most important relationship being stressed by the evangelists? (See Mark 3:34-35; John 19:25-27.)

6. What can we learn about the strength of Jesus' ministry by mention of Joanna (Luke 8:3; 24:10)?

7. Susanna (Luke 8:3) is one of many women who were able to provide essential and important support for the ministry of Jesus and the early believers. (See Acts 12:12; 16:13-14, 40; 17:4, 12, 34.) How could their presence in the Scriptures be highlighted to inspire women today?

8. Luke makes many mentions of the women who followed Jesus, witness his crucifixion, and even witnessed his resurrection. Why, then, do some scholars feel that Luke falls short of giving women their due? (Recall note nos. 1 & 2, chapter 5 of the commentary.)

Mary Magdalene (Luke 8:3; John 20:1-2, 11-18)

9. Before reading anything about Mary Magdalene in your commentary, jot down several words or phrases that you would usually associate with her.

10. a) What is the significance of Mary Magdalene being delivered of "seven demons" (Mark 16:9; Luke 8:2)? (See also Matt 12:43-45; Luke 11:24-26.)

    b) What long-term effects can we see in Mary that show she is completely delivered?

11. Put yourself in the place of Mary, a faithful disciple who goes to the tomb of Jesus only to find it empty (John 20:1-2). What would you have done? How would you have felt?

12. In what ways is Jesus shown to be a new ark of the covenant (John 20:12)? (See Exod 25:10, 16-22; Heb 9:4-5.)

13. Recall a time when you were grieving. What questions went through your mind? What gave you comfort?

14. a) When Jesus called Mary by name (John 20:16), how did it change her life?

   b) Do you feel that God has called you by name? What difference does it make in the way you live?

15. What are some of the reasons we hold on to the things and people we love? Why is it important to know when to let go (John 17:18)?

16. "Go" and "tell" are the basic instructions Mary receives from Jesus (John 20:17-18). Have you ever felt moved to leave something or some place that is comfortable because you had good news to share?

17. What is the significance of the statement, "I have seen the Lord" (John 20:18)? (See Luke 7:18-23; John 14:8-9; Acts 9:26-28; 1 Cor 9:1; 15:3-8.)

18. What are some practical ways that you can help to correct the false understanding that Mary Magdalene was a prostitute? What would you want others to know about her?

LESSON 6   Women and Discipleship, Part II

Matt 26:6-13; Mark 12:41-44; 14:3-9;
Luke 10:38-42; 21:1-4; John 11:1-44; 12:1-12
Women in the New Testament, pages 191–219

Review

1. What was the most important lesson you learned from the women studied last week?

Martha and Mary Welcome Jesus (Luke 10:38-42)

2. The story of Martha and Mary welcoming Jesus in their home is a familiar one.

   a) What difference does it make in your understanding of the story to become familiar with the church Luke was addressing with this story?

   b) In what ways is the commentary's evaluation of the story helpful to you personally?

3. What struggles do you see in your own parish or small faith community about the appropriate roles of women? How are these issues being addressed?

4. Is it necessary to choose sides between the Marthas and the Marys? Is it possible to create communities that appreciate both ways of living the Gospel, both ways of spreading the Good News?

Martha and Mary and the Raising of Lazarus (John 11:1-44)

5. If Jesus "loved Martha and her sister and Lazarus," why do you think he delayed in coming to their aid (11:5-6, 15)? Have you ever felt that God delayed in helping you?

6. Martha expresses a mixture of disappointment and hope (11:21-22) which Jesus uses to teach her and increase her faith (11:23-27). When have difficult moments been turned into important life lessons for you?

7. Upon seeing Mary weeping and being led to the tomb, we are told "Jesus wept" (11:35). If he knew he could raise Lazarus from the dead, why was Jesus weeping?

8. In your spiritual life, do you relate more strongly with Martha who ran to Jesus for help and learned to trust him, with Mary who shared her true emotions with Jesus, with Lazarus who was dead for a time but now lives, or with those who witness the scene and are confused?

9. Given the fact that Jesus spent time with Martha and Mary early in his ministry (Luke 10:38-42) and with them during the death and raising of their brother (John 11:1-44) and spent the final week of his life in Bethany too (John 12), how would you describe their relationship with him?

The Poor Widow (Mark 12:41-44; Luke 21:1-4)

10. Recall a time when you were able to learn a valuable lesson from watching what was going on around you (Mark 12:41-44). How can you regularly make time to reflect on the normal situations of life to see what God may be teaching you?

11. In what ways is the "poor widow" like Jesus? How does her contribution help to set the scene for Jesus' crucifixion (Mark 12:43-44; Luke 21:3-4)? (See Phil 2:5-8.)

12. Re-read the story of the widow in context with the previous story condemning the scribes who "devour the houses of widows" (Mark 12:38-40; Luke 20:45-47). Is Jesus praising the widow's gift outright, or is he using irony to criticize the scribes who demand sacrificial offerings from the poor when they themselves give only from their surplus?

13. What motivates you to give to the Church? What worthy uses of money is your parish engaged in? (See Matt 6:2-4; Luke 6:38.)

The Woman of Bethany Who Anointed Jesus
(Matt 26:6-13; Mark 14:3-9; John 12:1-12)

14. Why was anointing with oil significant in the Old Testament? (See Gen 35:14; Exod 29:1, 7; 30:26-29; 1 Sam 10:1; 16:11-13; 1 Kgs 19:15-16.)

15. Why is it significant that the woman anoints the head of Jesus (Matt 26:7; Mark 14:3)? (See 2 Kgs 9:2-3; Ps 23:5; Isa 61:1; Luke 4:18; Acts 4:27.)

16. Matthew and Mark describe the woman's actions but do not name her (Matt 26:7; Mark 14:3). John, on the other hand, identifies her as Mary of Bethany (John 12:1-3).

    a) What is the advantage of leaving her unnamed?

    b) How could John's naming of the woman have served to balance Luke's presentation of Mary? (See Luke 10:38-42.)

17. What do you believe motivated the disciples to object to the anointing (Matt 26:8-11; Mark 14:4-8; John 12:4-7)? Concern for the poor? Jealousy of her insight? Fear of appearing ignorant? Refusal to believe Jesus was approaching death? The wrong priorities? Something else?

18. What qualities of discipleship are found in this woman who anointed Jesus so close to the time of his arrest and execution? Is she a good role model?

LESSON 7   Women and Discipleship, Part III

John 2:1-12; 19:24-30; Acts 1:13-15; 9:36-43; 12:12; 13:13;
16:11-18, 40; 20:8; Rom 16; Phil 4:2-3
Women in the New Testament, pages 221–260

Review

1. How did last week's discussion or lecture help you to gain new insights about your own discipleship?

The Mother of Jesus (John 2:1-12; 19:24-30)
At Cana . . .

2. a) What associations should readers make when Jesus addresses his mother as "Woman" (2:4; 19:26)? (See Gen 2:23; 3:15, 20.)

   b) What is the "hour" he speaks of in 2:4 and 19:27? (See 4:23; 5:25; 7:30; 8:20; 12:23, 27; 13:1; 16:32; 17:1.)

3. Did Mary see something in Jesus that he was not yet ready to recognize in himself (2:3-5)? Has this ever happened to you?

4. In this scene at the wedding (2:1-12), what accents Mary's role as a mother, and what accents her role as a disciple?

5. Turning water into wine is the first of Jesus' signs (2:11). Why is this still a powerful sign? What does it suggest to you?

At the Crucifixion

6. Mary and a few others are found standing by the cross, near enough that Jesus can speak to them (19:25). This picture reminds us of how near Mary is to the suffering of her son. When has someone's real sharing in your suffering been especially important to you?

7. In his final moments, Jesus creates a bond between his mother and the "disciple whom he loved" (19:26-27). How will Jesus' concern affect the way the Church sees itself after his death and resurrection? (See Acts 2:42-47; Eph 2:19.)

8. In the Gospel accounts, Mary is always remembered in relation to her son. She receives attention (sometimes only a mention) at the annunciation and in her visit to Elizabeth, at the birth of Jesus and his later presentations at the Temple, at the wedding in Cana, and at the cross. Which scene in Mary's life could be symbolic for where you are in your relationship with Jesus?

Women of the Upper Room (Acts 1:13-15; 9:36-43; 12:12; 20:8)

9. A group of women, including Mary, are listed among those in the Upper Room (1:13-15). Is it logical to assume that they also witnessed the ascension of Jesus? (See 1:3-12.) Are there clues in the way the story is told?

10. What difference does it make to you to know that women were present in the Upper Room "devoting themselves to prayer" with the others gathered there (1:14), and in all likelihood present to be filled with the Holy Spirit (2:1-4)? What difference could it make to the Church?

11. The home of Mary, the mother of John Mark, is apparently one location where the church gathered in Jerusalem (12:12-17). What are some of the characteristics of a home that would enhance worship?

12. a) What Lukan characteristics are present in the story of Tabitha (9:36-43)?

    b) Tabitha is described as being "completely occupied with good deeds and almsgiving" (9:36) and significant enough in the community that men are sent to request help from Peter in a neighboring town (9:38). Have you ever seen a person's stature measured by his or her generosity and goodness? How could such a criteria change our culture?

13. For some Rhoda is a reminder that even confused or seemingly insignificant responses to God can help to advance the Gospel (12:11-17). Do you agree? If so, give an example.

Lydia and the Women of Philippi
(Acts 16:11-18, 40; Phil 4:2-3)

14. a) What kind of influence would Lydia have had in Philippi given her own background and occupation (Acts 16:11-18)?

    b) Lydia's conversion and baptism (the first in Europe) is followed by hospitality and leadership in the Christian community (Acts 16:15, 40). How has your own conversion come to bear fruit in your life?

15. Around the world, women are still exploited as the "slave girl" was, because of gender and poverty (Acts 16:16-18). What role can the Church and its leaders play in liberating these women? (See Luke 4:16-18.)

16. The disagreement between Euodia and Syntyche appears to have been significant enough to warrant Paul's intervention. Why is it important for leaders in the Church (those who "promote the Gospel") to come to "mutual understanding" (Phil 4:2-3)? (See John 17:20-21; Eph 4:1-6; 1 Pet 3:8.)

Phoebe and the Women of Rome (Rom 16)

17. a) Romans 16 does not describe in detail or defend the variety of roles women filled in the early Church. What does this indicate to you about the nature of their leadership?

   b) Have you known women whose ministry in the Church has served as an example? Describe their ministries and whether their gender had a positive or negative influence on the way they were received.

18. What is the most important lesson you learned about the women of the New Testament? What is the most important lesson you learned about your own faith in studying their lives?

NOTES